SKIN AND HAIR

Ron Thomas and Jan Stutchbury

Illustrated by Janine Evans

Irwin Publishing
Toronto, Canada

Our bodies are covered with skin.

4

Skin helps hold us together.
It can stretch and wrinkle.

6

Skin protects us.
It keeps germs and dirt out of our
bodies.

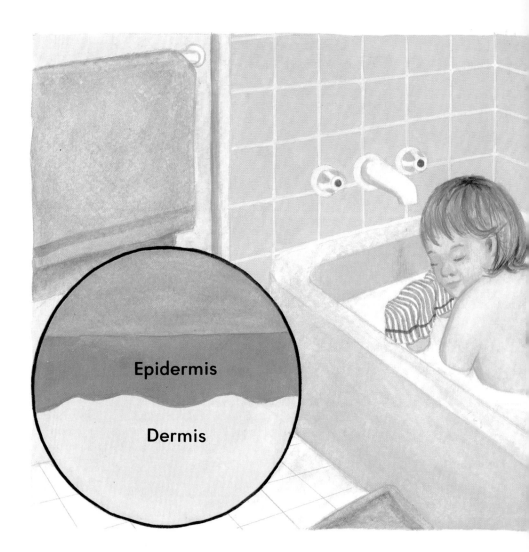

We have two layers of skin:
the epidermis and the dermis.
The epidermis is the top layer of skin.

New skin

Little bits of the epidermis rub off
when we wash.
New skin is growing all the time.

9

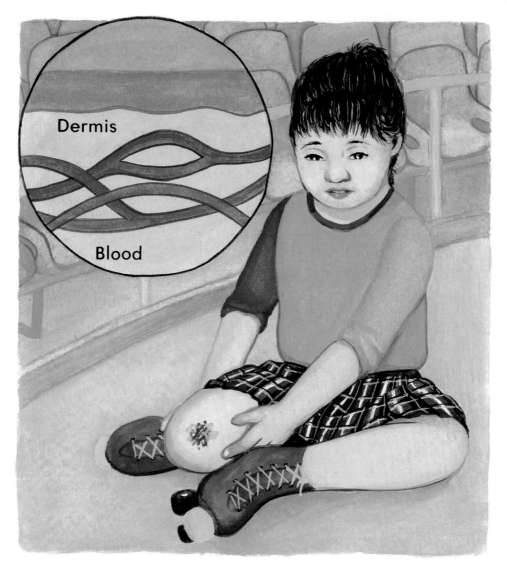

The dermis is the second layer of skin.
There's blood in the dermis.

If we cut the skin it will bleed.
We put a bandage over the cut to
keep the dirt out until the new skin
grows.

11

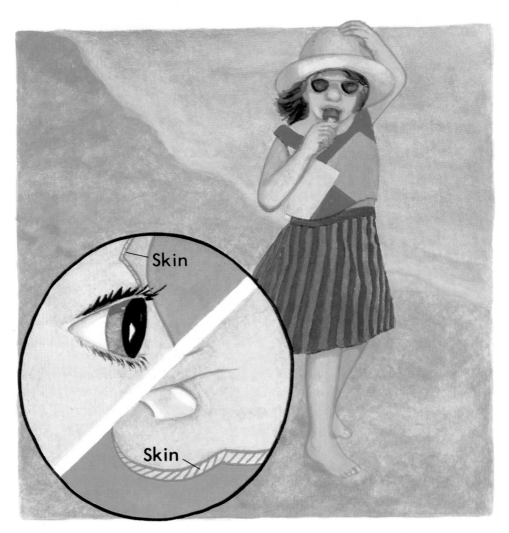

Some skin is thick and some is thin.
The skin on our feet is much thicker
than the skin on our eyelids.

12

The skin on our lips is very thin.
Blood in this thin skin
makes our lips red.

13

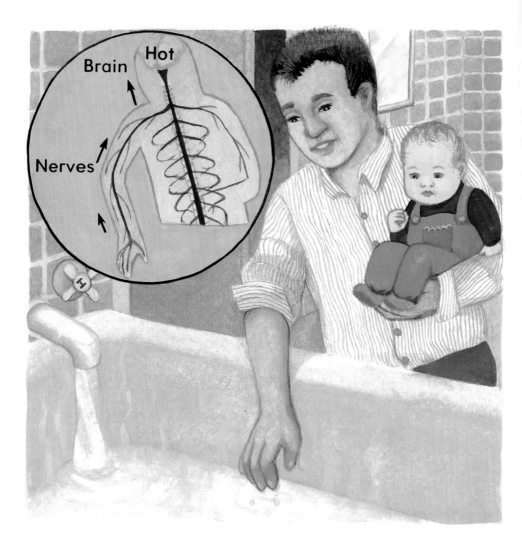

We can feel through our skin.
Nerves in the skin take messages
to the brain.

14

Our brain tells us if we are feeling
something rough or smooth,
or hard or soft, or hot or cold.

15

Fingernails and toenails are part
of our skin, too.
They protect our fingertips and toes.

16

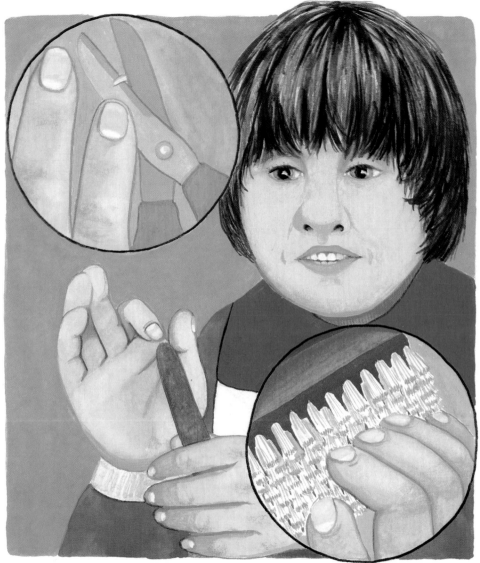

Our nails are growing all the time.
It doesn't hurt when we cut them.

Pores

We sweat when we are hot.
Sweat comes from tiny holes in our
skin called pores.

18

As the sweat dries, it makes us cool.
Sweat is also called perspiration.

Can you see your fingerprint?

We can make patterns with our
fingerprints.
Our feet can make prints, too.
These are our footprints.

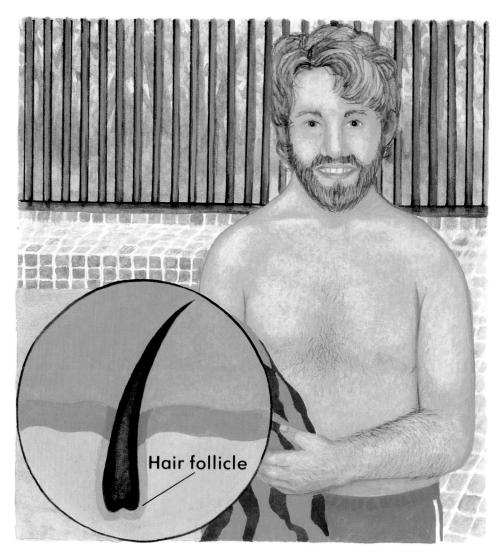

Hair follicle

Hair grows out of our skin.
It grows in a hair follicle

22

Hair follicles are different shapes.
Round follicles grow straight hair.
Oval follicles grow curly hair.
What shape follicles do you have?

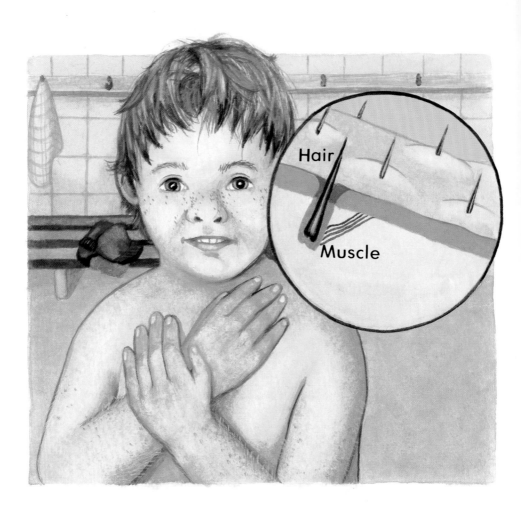

Hair

Muscle

Tiny muscles in the hair follicles
make our hairs move.
The muscles tighten when we are
cold. We get goose bumps.

24

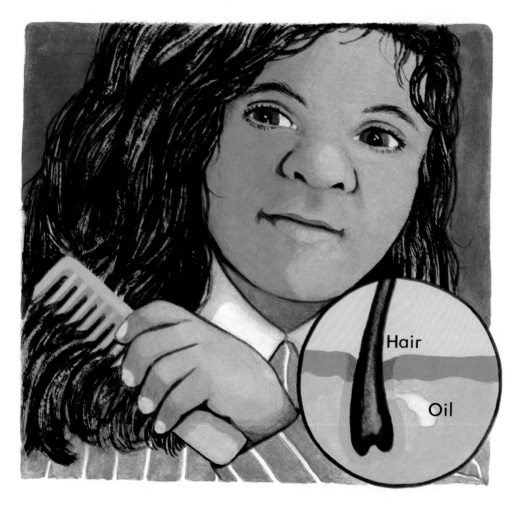

There is oil in the hair follicles, too.
It keeps our hair soft and shiny,
and stops our skin from becoming
dry.

Hair keeps our head warm in winter
and cool in summer.
People without hair are bald.
A hat protects their heads.

Washing and combing our hair
keeps it clean and healthy.

Skin and hair are different colors.
Who are you like?

Glossary

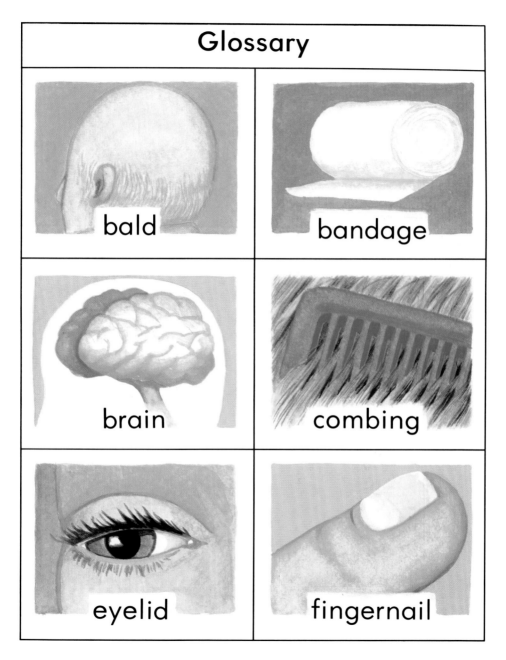

bald

bandage

brain

combing

eyelid

fingernail

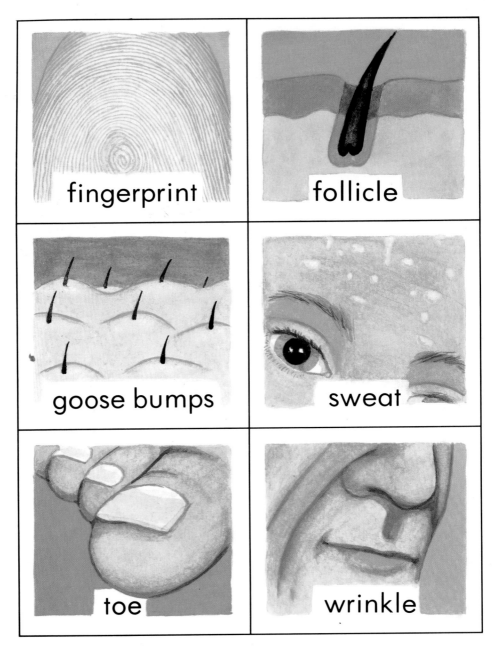

fingerprint

follicle

goose bumps

sweat

toe

wrinkle